D1092174

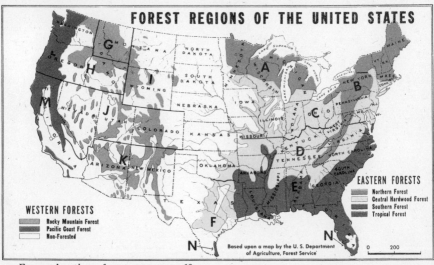

For explanation of map see page 60.

The BLUE BOOK of

TREES

A guide to the Ashes, Birches,
Elms, Maples, and other broad-leaved trees of North America

Text by P. J. VAN MELLE   Illustrations by RUDOLF FREUND

This is One of a Series of Two Tree Guide Books

WHITMAN PUBLISHING COMPANY • RACINE, WISCONSIN

As we stroll through the woods and look about us it soon becomes evident that there are a great many different kinds of trees. How to identify them is a fascinating hobby, and one which can be mastered with a little thought and study. Although it is impossible to include a guide to tree identification in a book of this size, a few of the pertinent differences between species can be described.

TREE SHAPES.—When grown in the open the crowns, or tops, of trees tend to develop characteristic shapes; oaks are wide-spreading; elms are vaselike; hickories are often oblong, etc.

LEAVES.—It is by the leaves that trees are divided into two great groups: *evergreens* (or softwoods) with persistent leaves, or leaves that stay on the tree for more than one year; and *deciduous* (or hardwoods), with leaves that fall every autumn. The evergreens are also called *narrow-leaved* and the deciduous trees are called *broad-leaved*. Leaves are further used in tree identification according to the number of blades to a single leaf, by their arrangement on the stem or branch, by their shape, type of margin, and quality of surface.

FLOWERS.—Except in a few cases, tree flowers are often inconspicuous and are available for study for only a short time each year, or may be absent for whole seasons. However, to the person who really wants to explore a whole new world, they offer interesting possibilities.

FRUIT.—The fruit of a tree is the ripened ovary together with any dried remnants of other parts that enclose the seed or seeds. Their various types are helpful clues in tree identification.

TWIGS.—Twigs together with their buds can be used for identification purposes during about nine months of the year. Trees usually have characteristic bud arrangement, bud covering, leaf scars, pith types and shapes, and twig color.

BARK.—Identification of trees by bark is probably the most difficult of all, as bark varies with tree age, site, and habitat, and the bark on no two trees in a woods will ever look exactly alike. However, the knowledge of the general characteristics of bark features will assist in tree identification.

Terms Used in This Book

Alternate—arrangement of leaves or leaflets on a stem singly, not opposite.

Axil—angle between upper surface of a branch or leaf and its stem.

Bloom—flower or flowering state; powdery coating on fruit or leaves.

Bract—scalelike leaf growing from stem at the base of the flower.

Calyx—outside part of flower, usually green.

Cleft—cut almost to center or to midrib of leaf.

Deltoid—triangular.

Elliptic—shaped like an elongated circle.

Epidermis—thin layer of outer cells of leaf which form the skin.

Fissure—narrow cleft or split in bark.

Follicle—dry, one-celled fruit or pod.

Globose—shaped like a globe.

Leaf Scar—mark left on the stem by leaf when it falls.

Lenticel—small pore in bark through which air can enter.

Lobe—rounded projection of a leaf.

Obovate—applied to leaves, etc., which are egg-shaped, broader at the tip.

Obovoid—applied to solids which are egg-shaped, broader at the tip.

Opposite—arrangement of leaves or leaflets in pairs, one on each side of a stem.

Ovate—applied to leaves, etc., which are egg-shaped in outline, broader at base.

Ovoid—applied to solids which are egg-shaped, broader at base.

Pinnate—applied to compound leaves having leaflets (pinnae) arranged on a single stem.

Sepal—a leaflike division of the calyx.

Sinus—space between two lobes of a leaf.

Spike—an elongated flower cluster.

Spine—sharp, woody growth on a stem.

Stipule—appendage on a leaf at base of the stem.

Stoma—small opening in leaf epidermis through which leaf breathes.

Strobile—a cone.

Whorl—arrangement of leaves or branches in a circle around a single stem.

BOX ELDER

Acer negundo   **Maple Family**

WIDELY distributed in the U.S., this tree favors margins of swamps and streams, but also thrives in drier soils; extensively planted in the West for windbreaks, on timber claims, and for shade. In the open, to 60 ft. high, with broad, irregular head. Bark dark gray with superficial ridges. Leaves pinnate, usually with 3 to 5 ovate, unevenly saw-toothed, often lobed and red-stalked leaflets to 4 in. long; autumn color, yellow. Flowers before leaves, yellowish-green; on male trees clustered on slender, silky, drooping stalks; on female, in drooping clusters. The fruit (winged "keys") remains into autumn, the fruit-stalks into winter. Wood light, fine-grained; used for interior trim, furniture, and woodenware. The MOOSE-WOOD *(A. pennsylvanicum)*, a shade-loving tree to 40 ft. high, grows on wooded hillsides. Occasionally, in the open, with narrow crown and ascending branches. Leaves obovate, 3-lobed in the upper part. Flowers following the leaves; in pendulous, hairless clusters to 6 in. long; yellowish-green. Wood has little practical use.

SILVER MAPLE

Acer saccharinum   **Maple Family**

THIS fast-growing wet-land tree, to over 100—sometimes to as much as 120—ft. high, thrives best in low bottom lands. The trunk branches off into several ascending limbs, forming a large, loose crown, ultimately with drooping outer branches. Bark on saplings smooth and silvery-gray; on old trunks brownish-gray, roughly scaly, and furrowed. Twigs reddish. Leaves to 7 in. long, deeply cleft by narrow sinuses into 5 slender, tapered, toothed lobes; green above, silvery-white beneath, pale yellow in autumn; stalks long, slender, often red. Flowers in very early spring, long before leaves; short-stalked in bundles, from clustered lateral buds; greenish-yellow; without petals. Winged fruit to 2 in. long, prominently veined, ripens in May; not opening at maturity. Much used for ornamental planting because of swift growth and handsome leaves. Close-grained, strong, rather hard wood is easily worked, used for furniture. Sap has a low sugar yield.

SUGAR MAPLE

Acer saccharum **Maple Family**

WIDELY distributed and abundant in well-drained, often rocky uplands and hillsides; often to 100 ft. or more; the trunk usually, at the base of the crown, branched off into a number of ascending main limbs. Crown is egg-shaped. Bark on old trunks dark gray, irregularly and roughly ridged. Buds pointed. Leaves to 5 in. wide or more, with 3 to 5 pointed main lobes, often toothed; in autumn usually yellow, sometimes orange-red. Flowers appear with leaves; small, greenish, on hairy stalks, in drooping clusters to 2½ in. long. Wood widely used for furniture, interior trim, keels of boats, etc. The sap, obtained in early spring, yields syrup and sugar. The OREGON MAPLE (*A. macrophyllum*) grows to about 90 ft., forms a solid head with the lower branches drooping. Bark on old stems brownish, with platelike scales. Twigs contain milky juice. Leaves to 12 in. wide on stalks to 12 in. long; dark, firm, lustrous; orange-red in autumn. Flowers appear with leaves; yellow, fragrant, in drooping clusters to 5 in. long. Wood as useful as that of Sugar Maple.

11

RED MAPLE

Acer rubrum **Maple Family**

WIDELY distributed over the eastern half of
the U. S. and southeastern Canada, favoring
bottom lands, banks of streams, and swamps,
sometimes forming almost exclusive forests.
Occasionally it attains a height of 100 ft. or
more in forests; in the open it has an oval
or rounded crown, ultimately with markedly
drooping side branches. Bark on old stems
dark gray, rough; on limbs smooth, silvery-
gray. Leaves 2 to 6 in. long, 3- to 5-lobed,
with triangular lobes and sinuses; brilliant red
in autumn. Flowers well before leaves, in
bundles, from clustered lateral buds; short-
stalked, greenish; often on short spurs; petaled: female red, male yellow or orange.
Fruit nearly 1 in. long, appearing in late
spring, on drooping stalks 2 to 4 in. long;
red. Wood valuable, extensively used in
making furniture, much of the Curly Maple
coming from this source. Sap gives maple
sugar although the yield is lower than that
of the Sugar Maple.

OHIO BUCKEYE

Aesculus glabra   **Horse Chestnut Family**

A SMALL tree, generally not over 30 ft. high, favoring rich, moist river banks ; in the open, forms a pyramidal crown. Bark on mature trunk gray, laid on in small, roughish plates. Twigs thick, straight. Terminal buds large and pointed, with scales enlarged to 2½ in. long in the spring. Leaves 5-fingered ; leaflets saw-toothed, elliptic to obovate, pointed ; hairy underneath when young ; yellowish-green ; yellow in autumn. Pale greenish-yellow flowers borne in terminal, erect usually one-sided clusters to 6 in. long, April to May ; stamens protruding. Fruit a green, obovoid to roundish husk with prickly surface, to 2 in. across ; contains 3 or more inedible brownish nuts to 1½ in. wide. Leaves and bark possess unpleasant odor. Wood light, soft, close-grained ; used in making artificial limbs and woodenware. The SWEET BUCKEYE (*A. octandra*), so called because of the absence of the disagreeable odor, grows up to 90 ft. high. Bark laid on in smoother, larger plates. Flowers tubular, yellow, showier ; stamens don't protrude. Husks have no prickles.

SHAD-BLOW
Serviceberry
Amelanchier canadensis   **Rose Family**

THIS is the tallest of our Juneberries, sometimes crowded up to 60 ft. high, abundant in fringes of upland woods which it enlivens in early spring with its white blossoms. In the open, to 30 ft. high or more, with oblong, round-topped crown, sometimes shrubby, not unlike a less stiff and more shapely pear tree. Branches markedly ascending in young trees, less so in old. Bark on young stems and branches smooth, gray with brownish stripes; on old trunks becoming scaly. Blossoms appear before or with foliage, in erect or nodding silky-haired clusters to 4 in. long. Reddish bracts soon fall off. Petals slender. Leaves similar to those of the pear; woolly at first, densely so beneath, less so above; stalks thin and slender. Fruit a purplish "berry" topped with a dry calyx; ripens in June; relished by birds. Called "Shad-blow" because the flowers appear when the shad starts up the rivers. Dark brown wood is strong, heavy, used in turnery for tool handles and, under the name "lancewood," for fishing rods.

HORSE CHESTNUT

Aesculus hippocastanum

Horse Chestnut Family

THIS very popular shade tree, first introduced in America from Europe over 200 years ago, is now found in practically every state of the U. S. Sometimes attaining a height of 75 or 80 ft., it is a familiar sight along the streets and in the parks of cities, with its roundish-pyramidal crown. Bark on mature trunks gray, laid on in irregular, somewhat loose plates. Twigs shiny brown, smooth, straight; terminal buds large and pointed. Leaves 7-fingered, to 8 in. long, on 4- to 7-in. stalks; obovate, widest near apex, tapering narrowly toward base; irregularly round-toothed. Flowers appear after leaves, in rather dense, showy pyramids of white mottled with red, a beautiful sight in spring. Fruit a green, globose husk, 2 to 3 in. in diameter, covered with spines; bearing 1 or 2 lustrous brown, irregularly hemispherical seeds, bitter and inedible. Bark is rich in tannin; the light, close-grained wood is used in the manufacture of artificial limbs, splints, and woodenware.

CHERRY BIRCH

Betula lenta   **Birch Family**

A GRACEFUL birch of moist, well-drained soils, to 75 ft. high (generally lower in the open). It forms a pyramidal or ovoid crown at first, ultimately becoming broader and rounder topped, with more or less pendulous outer branches. Bark on young stems and branches smooth, glossy, dark reddish-brown (suggestive of cherry, whence the name), with elongated transverse lenticels ("breathing" slits); on older trunks this smooth bark peels off in horizontal bands. Bark on mature trunks laid on in close, vertical flakes, dark brown in color. Twigs bright reddish-brown. Male spikes remain short in winter, lengthen early in spring to 3 or 4 in., opening purplish-yellow. Oblong-ovate leaves, to 5 in. long, taper to the apex, are roundish or somewhat heart-lobed at the base, sharply saw-edged; dark green above; golden-yellow in the autumn. Leafstalks to 1 in. long. Dark reddish-brown wood used for hubs, woodenware, furniture. Aromatic inner bark yields wintergreen oil. Birch beer is made of the sap.

GRAY BIRCH

Betula populifolia   **Birch Family**

A SMALL, rather frail and short-lived tree, rarely over 30 ft. high, this birch usually grows in clumps of several slanting stems, often bent by snow and ice. In the northern part of its range (northeastern U. S.) it grows in moist and swampy soils, and in the southern part on dryish, gravelly land. Bark chalky-white to grayish-white, with triangular black patches at the insertions and scars of long branches. Triangular-ovate leaves, to 3½ in. long. Male spikes to 3 in. Wood used for furniture, woodenware, and fuel. The RIVER BIRCH *(B. nigra)* is a shaggy birch of watersides and moist bottom lands in the eastern U. S., usually growing singly (not clumped), forming a pyramidal crown to 90 ft. high ; trunk sometimes branches near the base, more often higher up. Bark on young trees reddish-brown and lustrous, peeling off in horizontal bands ; on old trunks plated, not shaggy. Rhombic-ovate leaves, doubly saw-toothed, to 3½ in. long ; lustrous dark green above, whitish below. Light, strong wood used for furniture, woodenware.

17

PAPER BIRCH
Canoe Birch

Betula papyrifera   **Birch Family**

THIS beautiful white birch ranges across Canada and southward into the northern U. S., along water courses, in swamps, and on wooded slopes, in New England ascending into the higher altitudes. Distinguished from the eastern Gray Birch by its more robust, erect, single (not clumped) habit, its greater ultimate height—to 75 ft., and its bark, which peels off in horizontal strips. It forms a graceful pyramidal top, narrow in youth, wider with age. Young stems have smooth light brown bark and ascending branches; older trees have white to buff-colored bark, often black at base of trunk, and rather spreading branches, with drooping extremities. Ovate, pointed leaves are coarsely, doubly saw-toothed; to 4 in. long; ultimately firm and thick, hairless above; dark green, clear yellow in autumn. Male spikes to 4 in. long in spring. The bark, impervious to water, was used by Indians to cover canoes and wigwams, for baskets and paper. Wood used for woodenware, also an excellent fuel.

AMERICAN HORNBEAM

Carpinus caroliniana   **Beech Family**

A WIDE shrub or short-trunked tree of moist woodlands, sometimes forming thickets. In the open, usually a small tree to about 25 ft. high, having a broad, round-topped crown and wide-spreading branches, spreading horizontally into sweeps of dark, wiry twigs. Young trunks and main branches have smooth, tightly drawn, dark gray skin, suggestive of beeches, with musclelike corrugations. On old trunks bark is rather mottled and furrowed at the base. Winter buds pointed, ovate, brown. Ovate-oblong, pointed leaves, to 5 in. long, are irregularly, doubly saw-toothed, thin, dull green above, paler beneath, orange-scarlet in autumn. Leafstalks and veins on lower surface hairy. Pendulous male and female spikes appear with the leaves. Fruit clusters, to 4 in. long, on clear, slender stalks, bear a number of spreading, leafy, 3-lobed bracts to 1¼ in. long, the axil of each bract bearing a nutlet, subtended by 2 bractlets. Nuts about ⅛ in. long. The heavy, strong, tough wood is used for tool handles, woodenware, and fuel.

19

BITTERNUT

Carya cordiformis   **Walnut Family**

COMMON in wet woods and swampy land, sometimes to 90 ft. high, this tree has in the open a rather regular, broad crown, its gray-ish-brown bark netted with furrows and narrow ridges. Twigs slender, lustrous, orangey-brown. Buds yellow, rather slender and flattened. Leaves to 10 in. long, with 5 to 9 leaflets, apple-scented when crushed. Roundish fruit appears singly or 2 to 3 together. Husks thin. Roundish nuts are abruptly pointed, gray, the bitter kernel inedible. Wood used for tool handles, implements, hoops. The PECAN (*C. pecan*), also of wet-lands, grows to 150 ft. high with stout trunk to 4 ft. thick, and forms in the open a wide, rounded crown. Light reddish-brown bark is netted. Yellow buds pointed, downy. Leaves to 20 in. long, with 11 to 17 leaflets. Oblong-cylindrical fruit grows in spikes of as many as 10, up to 3 in. long, pointed, splitting along 4 winged seams. Cylindrical, pointed nuts to 2 in. long; shell thin, light brown with dark markings; kernel sweet; a profitable crop.

20

PIGNUT

Carya glabra   **Walnut Family**

This tree, with its characteristically graceful hickory crown, grows on uplands, ridges, and hillsides, 50 to 100 ft. high. Bark roughly netted with scaly ridges and furrows. End-buds spherical, side-buds smaller, pointed. Twigs slender. Leaves to 12 in. long; leaflets 3 to 7, mostly 5, dark olive green. Male spikes appear in May, to 7 in. long, in drooping clusters of 3. Pear-shaped to roundish fruit splits to about halfway down. Roundish nut is brownish, smooth, thin-shelled. Kernels generally not palatable. Wood used for tool handles, implements, hoops. The MOCKERNUT (*C. tomentosa*), also of rich uplands, to 50 or 60 ft. high or more, has downy twigs and leafstalks. Leaves, up to 20 in. long, with 7 to 9 leaflets, are fragrant when crushed; russet or yellow in autumn. Strongly scented husks are wingless. Somewhat flattened, light brown, 4-ridged nut is thick-shelled, hard to crack, often empty; kernel sweet but small. Wood used like that of Pignut. The downy winter buds distinguish the tree readily.

SHAGBARK HICKORY

Carya ovata **Walnut Family**

OCCASIONALLY exceeding 100 ft. in height, the Shagbark Hickory thrives best on low hillsides and along stream banks. In the open it has the characteristic hickory crown of slender, domed outline, with a skirt of drooping lower branches. The gray bark, laid on in hard, plate-like strips, springs away from the trunk, giving an appearance of shagginess. Twigs reddish-brown. Stout-stalked leaves, to 20 in. long, with 5, or rarely 7, leaflets ; dark green above, paler below. Flowers in May. Fruit, 1-3 together ; whitish nut has a sweet kernel. Wood highly valued for tool handles, implements, baskets, fuel, etc. On the BIG SHELLBARK HICKORY *(C. laciniosa)*, a sturdy, graceful tree of rich bottom lands, the gray bark is laid loosely in long, narrow shingles which remain close to trunk. Twigs orange-yellow. Leaves to 22 in., usually with 5 or 7 dark green leaflets. Male spikes in May, to 8 in. long, drooping, fringelike. Fruit grows singly or 2-3 together ; yellowish-white or reddish-white nut, kernel sweet. Wood used for tool handles, implements.

CHINQUAPIN

Castanea pumila **Beech Family**

THIS usually shrubby relative of the now almost extinct American Chestnut sometimes grows into a low-trunked tree, 40 to 50 ft. high, with a wide, round crown. Found on hillsides and uplands, occasionally in low, moist places. Gray bark shows a pale inner layer in the furrows. Buds lateral, downy. Oblong, pointed leaves are 2-ranked, forming flat sprays; to 5 in. long, coarsely saw-toothed or bristly; downy beneath; dull yellow in autumn. Cream-colored fragrant male flowers in late June or July in slender, erect spikes to 6 in. long; spikes sometimes also bear female flowers, usually 2 or 3 together in prickly envelopes, in the lower part. Nuts mature in densely spiny husks, 1 in each husk; dark brown, shiny; ¾ in. long, pointed, downy near tip; kernel finely flavored. Wood used for fence posts. The AMERICAN CHESTNUT *(C. dentata)*, now almost exterminated by a bark disease, used to grow to 100 ft. high. Only young growths, springing from stumps, are now seen. Leaves to 10 in. long, smooth beneath. Nuts 2 or 3 in a husk.

23

COMMON CATALPA

Catalpa bignonioides   **Rignonia Family**

A COARSELY branched tree, to 60 ft. high, late to leaf out, growing in river margins and moist woods of the Southeast, widely naturalized because of its handsome flowers. Short-trunked, with a broad, dome-topped, irregularly pyramidal crown. Brownish-gray bark is slightly furrowed and scaly. Twigs thick. Small, spherical winter buds placed above circular scars of leafstalks. Leaves in pairs or in whorls of 3, ovate, usually heart-lobed at base, to 8 in. long and about as wide, downy underneath; light green; ill-smelling when crushed. Flowers in June or July, in multi-flowered, erect clusters to 10 in. long, white with yellow and purplish markings within, fragrant. Long, drooping green pods split in winter into 2 "valves." The WESTERN CATALPA (*C. speciosa*) of the Ohio River basin, to 90 ft. high, forms a more slender crown. Leaves larger, not ill-scented. Fewer flowers in a cluster, larger, with lower lobe notched (unlike Common Catalpa). Wood very durable in ground, used for railroad ties, fence posts, etc.

24

COMMON HACKBERRY

Celtis occidentalis   **Elm Family**

ABUNDANT in the Mississippi basin this tree
grows mostly in moist bottom lands but often in
higher, drier soils. Sometimes well over 100
ft. high, usually much lower; in the open, has
an oblong crown and more horizontal, less
drooping branch manner than the related
American Elm. Bark on young trunks and
branches smooth, gray, ruffled with black em-
bossings, more densely so on old trunks. Buds
small, ovate. Twigs sometimes slightly hairy.
Ovate, pointed, saw-toothed leaves, to about
4 in. long, are usually hairless; somewhat shiny
above; pale below and sometimes hairy on the
veins; autumn color pale yellow. Flowers,
appearing in May, are inconspicuous. Orange
to purplish fruit, about ¼ in. diam., often remains into winter, is eaten by birds. Heavy,
soft, coarse wood used for cheap furniture,
fences, etc. The MISSISSIPPI HACKBERRY (*C.
laevigata*) is a lower, rounder-topped tree with
generally untoothed, markedly unequal-sided,
longer-tapered, hairless leaves; bark similar
to Common Hackberry.

25

REDBUD
Judas Tree

Cercis canadensis   **Pea Family**

A CHARMING little tree of well-drained and open woodlands in the eastern U. S., as far north as New Jersey. Often drawn up to a spindly height of 35 ft. in the woods, usually much lower when isolated, with a wide, low, horizontal, domed crown. Trunk rarely over 12 in. thick, covered with small, smoothish, close, dark reddish-brown scales. Branches smooth, gray-brown, brittle, bilaterally ramified. Broadly heart-shaped to roundish leaves are 2-ranked, in flattish sprays, from alternate buds, apex bluntly pointed to rounded, to 5 in. long; somewhat leathery; glossy deep green, in autumn yellow. Flowers before leaves, bright rosy-purple, shaped like pea-flowers, to ½ in. long, borne on slender stalks in bundles of 4 to 8 along the bare branches. Thin, flat pods, 2½ to 3½ in. long, maturing in September, hang on, brown, into winter. Yellowish-brown, brittle wood economically unimportant. This spring-flowering tree occurs commonly together with the Flowering Dogwood and blooms together with it.

FLOWERING DOGWOOD

Cornus florida **Dogwood Family**

THIS lovely spring-flowering little tree is abundant in well-drained coppices and woodland fringes through the eastern U. S. In the woods, sometimes a lanky tree to 35 ft.; usually much lower in the open, with a short trunk and a picturesque sweep of branches to 25 ft. wide, having in winter a lacy pattern of twigs and buds. Bark on saplings brownish, smooth; on old trunks in small, dark gray flakes, with tan-colored inner layer underneath. Flower buds roundish, knobby in winter. Pointed, generally ovate leaves opposite, 3 to 6 in. long; autumn color scarlet. Greenish, tiny flowers growing in small clusters, surrounded by 4 very showy bracts enfolding the bud in winter and becoming enlarged and snow-white or pinkish in the spring. Bracts obovate, to more than 2 in. long, with short-pointed apex, usually notched. Scarlet berries, about 1/3 in. long, ripen in autumn, are eaten by birds. Wood useful for tool handles. Bark employed medicinally; root-bark yields a scarlet dye.

27

AMERICAN ELM

Ulmus americana **Elm Family**

A STATELY elm, in moist bottom lands to 120 ft. high, generally lower in higher, drier soils; with tall, clear trunk, divided high up into several outward-flaring limbs supporting a shallowly domed crown with gracefully pendulous extremities. It is planted traditionally on New England village greens. Narrow-crowned forms sometimes occur. Bark gray, ridged. Greenish-red flowers appear in early spring, in bundles on slender, drooping stalks; small, winged fruits ripen and fall before leaves are fully grown. Obovate, unsymmetrical, sawtoothed leaves, to 6 in. long, grow in 2 ranks, forming flat sprays; margin fringed; yellowish in autumn. Leafstalks short. Wood used in boatbuilding, for flooring, barrels, hubs; durable in soil. The ROCK or CORK ELM *(U. thomasi)* of dry, rocky uplands forms a narrow, oblong crown to 70 ft. high, with rugged, lateral, corky branches. Buds large, pointed, hairy. Flowers in clusters. Leaves to 4 in. long; bright yellow in autumn. Wood prized for hubs, used for farm implements.

SLIPPERY ELM

Ulmus fulva   **Elm Family**

A TREE of rich bottom lands, with a graceful
broad-topped crown, sometimes irregular, in
the open, to about 60 ft. high, the trunk often
divided close to the base. Bark on mature
trunks brownish-gray, with shallow fissures
and narrow loose flakes. Twigs rough, red-
brown or orange. Buds large, blunt, rusty-
hairy. Flowers densely clustered, on short,
erect stalks. Wing of the fruit roundish. Taper-
pointed, saw-toothed leaves to 8 in. long;
densely hairy beneath; dull yellow in autumn.
This elm is distinguished by its large, rough
leaves. Boys like to carve out the sweet, fragrant inner bark, thereby injuring the tree. This
inner bark is often used for various medicinal
purposes. Wood used for railroad ties, posts,
sills, implements. The WINGED or WAHOO ELM
(*U. alata*) of uplands and swamp margins
forms a regular, oblong to obovoid crown, to
45 ft. high, with corky branches, less rugged
than the Cork Elm (page 28). Flowers in
scanty clusters. Leaves to 2½ in. long; hairy
beneath; dark green; dull yellow in autumn.

29

PERSIMMON

Diospyros virginiana   **Ebony Family**

OCCURRING in woods and fields and hedgerows, in light or richer soils, this tree rarely attains a height of 100 ft., usually 40 to 50 ft. In the open, it has a graceful, narrow or wider round-topped crown. Bark dark gray, laid on in thick squarish or oblong plates, in a blocked pattern. Twigs reddish; downy at first. Buds small, pointed. Leaves alternate, to 6 in. long, ovate to elliptic, tapering to a point, thick and leathery; lustrous dark green when full-grown, purplish-red in autumn. Leafstalks short and stout. Small, very fragrant, yellowish-green flowers in May or June, male and female on separate trees. Male flowers in clusters of 3, female solitary. Fruit a juicy, roundish berry to 1½ in. diam., at first hard and green, later soft and orangey, sometimes red-cheeked, not palatable until fully ripe and mellowed by early frost, of variable eating quality. Reddish-brown, heavy, hard, close-grained wood used in turnery, for shoe lasts, tools, shuttles.

AMERICAN BEECH

Fagus grandifolia   **Beech Family**

THIS tree's smooth, lustrous gray bark and graceful habit make it easily recognized at a distance in winter. It grows abundantly in the eastern U. S., often forming groves and forests in rich uplands or bottom lands and on hillsides. Sometimes to more than 100 ft. high, but generally not over 75 ft.; slender, with tall clear trunk when crowded. Less tall in open, with short clear trunk and broad, round-topped crown, usually with a skirt of sweepingly pendulous lower branches. Winter buds long, pointed, brown. Ovate-oblong, pointed, saw-toothed leaves to 5 in., dark green above, paler below, yellow to russet in autumn. Shiny brown triangular nut to ¾ in. long falls at maturity from a woody, prickly case which opens in autumn into 4 "valves." Nuts harvested to some extent in northern parts and form important food supply for woods animals. Bark used in manufacture of skin ointments. Hard. tough wood used in manufacture of furniture.

31

WHITE ASH

Fraxinus americana   **Olive Family**

A VALUABLE timber tree of rich slopes and well-drained bottom lands. In the forest rarely attains a height of 120 ft; isolated trees lower, with broad pyramidal or ovoid crowns. Gray to brownish-gray bark, netted into diamond-shaped meshes by braided ridges. Branchlets dark green to brownish-green, hairless, shiny. Buds dark brown, plump. Opposite, pinnate leaves appear late in spring, usually with 7 slender-stalked, hairless leaflets; dark green above, whitish below; mauve-purple or yellowish in autumn. Flowers before leaves, inconspicuous, male and female on separate trees; followed by long-stalked, pale or rosy-tinted clusters of winged fruit, maturing in September. Fruit, with terminal wing, to 2 in. long. Weak, elastic wood; used for frames of vehicles, oars, interior finish, tool handles. The BLUE ASH (*F. quadrangulata*) of limestone ridges has scaly bark, in large shaggy plates on old trunks. Twigs 4-angled. Leaflets to 11, saw-edged. Flowers 2-sexed. Wood used for flooring. Inner bark yields a blue dye.

32

HONEY LOCUST

Gleditsia triacanthos **Pea Family**

A USUALLY thorny tree of rich woodlands, to 140 ft. high in the woods, in the open having a graceful, obovoid, flat-topped crown. Bark dark gray, smooth, on old trunks firmly scaly. Winter buds minute, 3 or 4 together, one above another. Stout, ultimately branched thorns, to 4 in. long, are set above leaf-axils and crowded at base of main limbs. Leaves once- or twice-pinnate, to 10 in. long; 8 to 14 pinnae, each with 20 to 30 short-stalked, oblong-lance-shaped, blunt-tipped, somewhat saw-toothed leaflets. Main leafstalk downy. Leaves green above, paler beneath, yellow in autumn. Inconspicuous greenish flowers appear in June in clusters to 3 in. long, male and female in separate clusters or on separate trees. Long, lustrous, purplish, ultimately brown pods to 18 in. long, hang on into winter; contain numerous hard, flat seeds and a pulp which is sweet in summer (the "honey" of the Honey Locust which boys and girls go climbing after). Hard, heavy, durable wood; used for hubs, handles, fence posts, railroad ties.

KENTUCKY COFFEE TREE
Gymnocladus dioicus   **Pea Family**

A HANDSOME, common but not abundant tree, in rich bottom lands, sometimes in the forest, to 100 ft. high, with tall, clear trunk. Of variable habit in the open, but usually with rather narrow crown. Easily recognized in summer by its huge twice-pinnate leaves, and in winter by the stout, bony branches which have earned it such names as "skeleton tree" in other countries. Old trunks covered with prominent, thick, rough, dark gray scales. Leaves rosy-tinted when they unfold, later green, yellow in autumn; to 2 ft. long or more, with 6 to 14 pinnae, each having 12 to 24 or more short-stalked leaflets, at first downy underneath. Pinnae shed before main leaf-axils. Flowers in terminal clusters in June, male and female separate or on separate trees, female clusters to 10 in. long, male shorter. Flowers inconspicuous, greenish-white. Brownish, heavy, thick-walled pods, to 10 in. long, contain several roundish, flat beans and a sweet pulp. Pioneers used beans as a coffee substitute.

BLACK WALNUT

Juglans nigra   **Walnut Family**

A LARGE tree of rich forests, often to 150 ft. Lone trees shorter, with broad, round tops and tall trunks. Brown bark deeply furrowed. Twigs, buds, leaf-linings, downy. Young parts aromatic. Leaves to 2 ft. long; leaflets, 13 to 23, asymmetrical at base. Male spikes to 6 in. long, drooping, greenish, from old wood; female flowers on new growth. Fruit single or 2 or 3 together, roundish, husks not splitting, to 2 in. across. Nuts to 1½ in., deeply grooved, divided into 4 compartments at base; kernel savory. Purplish-brown wood, with satiny finish; highly valued for furniture, interior finish, veneers, gunstocks, etc. Bark rich in tannic acid, and yields, as do husks, a yellow dye. The BUTTERNUT (*J. cinerea*) of moist lowlands, rarely over 75 ft. high, has a short, stout trunk and wide-flung crown often broader than high. Bark gray. Yellowish-green leaves to 30 in. long with 11 to 17 symmetrical leaflets. Fruit clustered, 2 to 5. Nuts more slender and tapered, 2-celled. Wood coarser but durable. Sweet sap may be boiled down to a syrup.

35

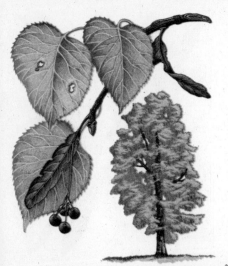

AMERICAN BASSWOOD
Linden

Tilia americana   Linden Family

In RICH, moist, well-drained lowland woods and slopes, this tree sometimes reaches a height of 125 ft., with a columnar trunk to more than 3 ft. thick; isolated trees usually lower, with symmetrical, broadly ovoid crowns. Bark on mature trunks grayish, netted with ridges and grooves; branches smooth, grayish. Winter buds plump, reddish. Leaves alternate, spreading into flat sprays; to 8 in. long, broadly ovate, often heart-lobed at base, abruptly tapering to a point; coarsely saw-toothed; light green above, paler below, dull yellow in autumn. Leaves appear late, shed early. Small, yellowish, fragrant flowers appear in July in long-stalked drooping clusters. Fruit a woody pea-sized ball with 2 or 3 seeds; the entire cluster drooping ultimately, stalk and all, with a large leaflike bract for a propeller. Soft, light wood used for furniture, cooperage, wood carving, paper pulp, charcoal; bees make a choice honey from flowers. The WHITE BASS-WOOD *(T. heterophylla)* has leaves coated underneath with white to rusty woolly hairs.

SWEET GUM
Liquidambar styraciflua Witch Hazel Family

A HANDSOME bottom-land tree of the eastern U. S., growing, in Southern forests, to 140 ft. high. It is generally lower in the open, with a symmetrical oblong-pyramidal crown, broader in old age; its limbs stout, the lower spreading, the upper rising. On old trunks, reddish-brown or gray bark is netted, with shallow furrows, longish flat scales; on limbs, gray, with warty ridges. Lighter branches and twigs rather corky, the twigs winged. Deep green, shiny, aromatic leaves, about 7 in. long and wide, have saw-toothed, taper-pointed lobes; in autumn purplish, streaked with crimson and orange. Inconspicuous flowers appear in May, female in long-stalked, roundish heads, maturing into woody, prickly fruit-balls, 1½ in. across, releasing in October a sawdust-rain of undeveloped seeds with a few winged fertile ones. Close-grained, heavy, reddish-brown, dark-striped wood is capable of a fine polish, used for exterior finish, shingles, construction timbers, railroad ties; selected grades used as Satin Walnut. Resinous sap is used in medicines and perfumes.

37

TULIP TREE
Yellow Poplar
Liriodendron tulipifera Magnolia Family

ONE of the tallest—to 150 ft. high, with trunk clear of branches halfway up—and most valuable of eastern U. S. forest trees prefers deep, rich, moist soils. Lone trees generally much lower, with regular, pyramidal crowns. Bark somewhat brownish-gray, with netted ridges. Leaves to 5 in. long, variously 4-lobed, often sub-lobed, are lustrous bluish-green on upper side, paler beneath, clear yellow or russet in autumn; leafstalks to 4 in. long. Greenish-white flowers with orange centers appear after leaves, decorative but not brilliant, 3 to 4 in. wide, with 6 petals; the 3 sepals soon fall off. Fruit, a brownish cone 2 to 3 in. long, bears many winged "follicles" which fall off at maturity, leaving, in winter, only the bare shaft surrounded by an outer whorl of dry, seedless balls in a flowerlike pattern (easily identifying tree in winter). Soft, fine-grained wood is easily worked and bent; used for furniture, boatbuilding, interior trim, shingles, and woodenware.

OSAGE ORANGE

Maclura pomifera **Mulberry Family**

THIS native of Texas, Arkansas, and Oklahoma prefers rich, moist soils, but, adaptable to drier soils, is widely naturalized. Lone trees to about 60 ft. high, with trunks to 3 ft. thick, branching off to a few heavy, orange-colored limbs, topped by symmetrical, rounded, rather open crowns. Bark on old trunks orange-brown, deeply furrowed between irregular, bold ridges. Young twigs downy; orange-brown in winter. Stout spines, to ½ in. long, placed above leaves. Buds deeply sunk, spirally coiled. Ovate to lance-oblong, taper-pointed leaves, to 5 in. long; lustrous bright green, in autumn clear yellow; contain a bitter, milky sap. Small greenish flowers in June, male and female on separate trees, male in short sprays, female in dense, roundish heads. Fruit a green, orangelike ball, to 5 in. across, with embossed surface, ripening in September. Orange-yellow wood, strong, durable, tough: used for poles, ties, paving blocks, hubs. Indians made bows of branches. Bark yields tannic acid and a yellow dye.

CUCUMBER TREE

Magnolia acuminata   **Magnolia Family**

THIS tallest of our magnolias—sometimes crowded upward to 90 ft.—favors stream-washed uplands, hillsides. In the open, generally with sturdy, oblong, round-topped crown, and grayish-brown trunk with braided, narrow ridges. Buds silky. Leaves to 10 in., ultimately downy only on lower side, yellow in autumn. Inconspicuous yellowish-green flowers in May, bell-shaped, to 3 in. long. Conelike fruit at first resembles a small green cucumber, later releases scarlet seeds that dangle on elastic threads. Wood used for flooring. The LARGE-LEAVED MAGNOLIA *(M. macrophylla)*, rarely over 40 ft. high, has wide-branched crown, gray-barked trunk; leaves to 30 in. long, heart-lobed at base, white-downy below. Cream-white flowers, to 12 in. long, are very fragrant. Fruit-cone rounded, rosy. Seeds scarlet. The SWEET BAY *(M. virginiana)*, which grows in swamps, is shrubby and deciduous in the North, evergreen in the South, growing to 50 ft. high or more. Leaves oblong, to 6 in. long. Flowers cream-colored, rose-scented.

WILD CRAB APPLE
Sweet Crab

Malus coronaria   **Rose Family**

A LITTLE tree of well-drained woodlands, road-
sides, and pasture lots, related to the apple,
and resembling it in habit, bark, and broadly
petaled blossom. Often with forked trunk, it
reaches, rarely, a height of 30 ft., with broadly domed crown, its often contorted branches
set with short spurs ending in a thornlike
point. Young twigs downy. Ovate to nearly
triangular, saw-toothed leaves, to 4 in. long,
are generally bluntly pointed, sometimes lobed
on sterile shoots, generally ultimately hairless,
or with veins downy below, yellow in autumn.
White or pinkish blossoms appear after leaves
in 5- to 6-flowered clusters on hairless stalks,
spicily fragrant, to 2 in. across. Fruit short-
ened-spherical with ribbed apex; to 1½ in.
across; green, hard, acid; excellent for jellies.
In the PRAIRIE CRAB *(M. ioensis)*, the twigs are
downy, the calyx, leafstalks, and flower stalks
persistently woolly-hairy. Rose-scented flowers
generally 2 or 3 together on stout, 2-inch stalks.
Fruit spherical, green, waxy, fragrant.

41

RED MULBERRY

Morus rubra **Mulberry Family**

OUR only native mulberry grows in rich bottom lands and on low hillsides, to 70 ft. high; generally lower in the open, its short trunk and ascending limbs supporting a tallish, round-topped crown. Bark on young stems and limbs orange-brown, on old stems—deep-furrowed between long, corky ridges suggestive of willow. Young twigs downy. Alternate broadly ovate, sharply saw-toothed leaves, abruptly narrowed to a point, are often oddly lobed on the shoots; rather dark and mostly rough above, duller and downy below. Lateral veins connected near the margins with rounded arches. Foliage clear pale yellow in autumn. Juicy, sweet fruit, like a dark purple blackberry, appearing June-July, is seldom harvested, relished by birds. Yellow, soft, coarse-grained, but durable wood; used for boat-building, cooperage, posts. Indians made a coarse cloth from bast fiber. The WHITE MULBERRY *(M. alba),* is widely naturalized in the U. S. Its shiny, lighter green, less broadly oval leaves are not abruptly narrowed at apex. Fruit whitish to violet.

TUPELO
(Sour, or Black, Gum)
Pepperidge

Nyssa sylvatica   **Tupelo Family**

Most northerly and least aquatic of our tupelos. Trunk rises unbranched to 90 ft., often becoming hollow and decrepit, devoid of lower branches, with a small cylindrical crown high up. In youth, habit is similar to that of the young Pin Oak; branches with short spurs, lower ones drooping, upper horizontal. Bark gray, soon breaking into a network of thick, flat or corky ridges. Winter buds project outward. Leaves alternate, to 5 in., ovate to obovate, apex rounded to somewhat pointed, mostly entire, ultimately hairless and lustrous above, whitish below; like polished copper in autumn. Flowers not showy. Fruit blue-black, ovoid, to ½ in. long; 1 or several on a thin stalk; ripe in October. Wood used for woodenware, fruit boxes, hubs. The more aquatic WATER GUM *(var. biflora)* bears 1 or 2 fruits on a stalk. Trunk gradually widens at base. In the COTTON GUM *(N. aquatica)* base of trunk is greatly swollen. Young leaves fluffy with cotton; fruit borne singly.

HOP HORNBEAM
Ironwood

Ostrya virginiana **Birch Family**

WIDELY distributed over the eastern U. S., this tree reaches its greatest development in rich woods, where it grows to 60 or 70 ft., with a trunk to 2 ft. thick or more. It often ascends into higher, wooded, gravelly hillsides, even flourishes in windy, cold exposures. A tough-wooded, shapely, round-topped tree, with spreading to drooping horizontally ramified branches, it suggests both birch and beech in winter. In the open it usually grows to less than maximum height, with short trunk. Bark smooth and lustrous on young stems and branches; on old trunks, brownish-gray, laid on in long, narrow, scaly ridges. Leaves oblong-lance-shaped; pointed; finely, doubly saw-toothed; 3 to 5 in. long; to 2 in. wide; yellowish-green; clear yellow in autumn. Short leafstalks. Male spikes drooping in spring, about 2 in. long; female developing into drooping, long-stalked trusses of bladderlike envelopes of pale green leafy bracts, within which the small, hard nutlets mature. Wood makes good tool handles, durable fence posts.

44

SORREL TREE

Sourwood

Oxydendrum arboreum   **Heath Family**

On the lower, rich, wooded slopes of the Alleghanies, occasionally a slender-stemmed tree to 70 ft.; usually lower, and, in the eastern part of its distribution, in moister soils. Lone trees generally upward of 25 ft., with narrow, oblong to obovoid crowns. Bark on old trees reddish-gray, laid on in long, smoothish, scaly ridges. Buds red, small. Twigs sometimes slightly downy. Leaves alternate, 3 to 8 in. long, elliptic to lance-shaped, tapering to a point; finely, irregularly saw-toothed; lustrous deep green above, whitish below; brilliant scarlet in autumn. Leafstalks 3 to 5 in. long. Flowers whitish, attractive to bees, about ¼ in. long, urn-shaped; open in July, in terminal, drooping clusters, draped effectively over outside of tree even after seed capsules have developed; capsules remain into winter. Reddish-brown, fine-grained wood used in turnery, for tool handles. Leaves and young shoots rather acid—hence the name "Sourwood"—and thirst-quenching; of some tonic and medicinal value.

45

SYCAMORE
Buttonball
Platanus occidentalis   **Plane Tree Family**

SAID to be the tallest deciduous tree in North America: to over 150 ft. in bottom lands of the Ohio and the Mississippi; it usually follows stream courses. Old trees usually have tall, clear trunks; wide, irregular crowns. Branches angularly crooked. Bark often dark and fissured at base; mottled tan and green higher up; on upper limbs often chalky-white; on young stems olive green, shedding in thin shells to bare tan-colored new bark. Buds hidden in summer under swollen, hollow leaf-bases. Leaves about 8 in. wide, with 3 to 5 shallow, toothed lobes, wider than long; shed a cottony fluff in spring. Seeds densely packed into 1-in. balls, maturing in September; swinging, generally singly, on long, thin stalks. Seeds usually bale out singly on fluffy parachutes. Strong but warping wood used for butchers' blocks, interior trim, cigar boxes, etc. The CALIFORNIA SYCAMORE *(P. racemosa)* has deeper, narrow, sparsely toothed leaf-lobes, and bristly, stalkless seed-balls, 2 to 7 together; leaves woolly below.

COTTONWOOD

Populus deltoides **Willow Family**

THIS large poplar, widely distributed over most of the U. S., prefers bottom lands and moist stream banks. When not crowded, it forms a rather broad, loose, often round-topped crown, usually on a framework of a few stout main limbs. Occasionally to 100 ft. high, with trunk 6 ft. or more in diameter, it grows largest and most abundantly in the interior. Bark on old stems ashen-gray, with thick, vertical, corky ridges. Twigs hairless, somewhat angular. Buds brownish, pointed, sticky. Triangular-ovate to broadly ovate leaves, to 5 in. long, taper to a point ; roundish base faintly heart-lobed or lopped off ; bluntly toothed margin densely fringed with fine hairs. Flowers in drooping spikes, before leaves : male 3 to 5 in. long, reddish ; female 6 to 8 in. Light, soft wood ; used for pulp, packing cases, fuel. The SOUTHERN COTTONWOOD *(P. delt.* var. *missouriensis)* has more prominently angled twigs, leaves more nearly ovate than deltoid, to 5½ in. long, usually longer than broad, more finely toothed.

LARGE-TOOTHED ASPEN

Populus grandidentata   **Willow Family**

INHABITING rich, moist, sandy and loamy slopes and stream margins, this tree grows to about 60 ft., forming in the open a narrow ovoid, often round-topped crown. Greenish-gray bark smooth but somewhat fissured near base of stem. Stout twigs ultimately reddish or orange-brown. Buds ovoid, gray-downy. Ovate to roundish, pointed, coarsely, unevenly toothed leaves, to 4 in. long, held on slender, flattened stalks which cause blades to quiver with the slightest breeze. Light wood used mainly for pulp and excelsior. The QUAKING ASPEN *(P. tremuloides)* inhabits lighter soils, reaching far northward; commonly not over 60 ft. high, but occasionally to 90 ft. Often short-lived; the most graceful of our poplars, forming a loose, round-topped crown. Smooth, pale yellowish-bronze bark; more or less fissured on old trunks. Twigs slender, reddish-brown. Ovate or roundish, pointed, finely toothed leaves, to 2½ in. long, are always aflutter; dull yellowish-green below; yellow in autumn. Wood used for pulp.

BALSAM POPLAR

Populus tacamahaca   **Willow Family**

RANGING far north into Canada, this tree there attains its greatest development, occasionally reaching a height of 100 ft.; with trunk to 6 ft. in diameter. It favors the proximity of streams and swamps in its range across the northern U. S. In the open it forms a narrow, irregularly pyramidal crown, on a framework of a few stout, ascending limbs. Bark gray, with broad, uneven ridges on old stems. Buds long, pointed, sticky. Thick, firm leaves are ovate to lance-ovate, pointed, generally broadly wedge-shaped at base; to 5 in. long; with fine, pointed teeth; hairless at maturity; shiny green above, whitish below, yellow in autumn; stalks to 5 in. long. Flowers before leaves; male and female on separate trees, as in all poplars; spikes drooping, male to 3 in. long, female to 6 in. Wood used for pulp. Fragrant wax on buds and young leaves (source of name Balsam Poplar) is harvested by bees in spring, also used by Indians to seal birch canoes and for other purposes.

BLACK CHERRY
Wild Cherry

Prunus serotina   **Rose Family**

THE largest of our wild cherries, this tree occurs in varied soils and conditions in the East. Height to 90 ft. (usually less); crown oblong, round-topped. Bark on trunk and limbs shiny dark brown, with transverse slits; peels in transverse, leathery, curled bands, as in birches; on old trunks sometimes scaly. Twigs reddish. Buds slender, pointed. Oval to oblong leaves, tapering to a point, saw-toothed; reddish when young, later lustrous green above, paler below, yellow in autumn; firmly textured. White flowers appear after leaves; 1/3 in. across; in 6 in. long clusters, erect when in flower, nodding in fruit, with a few leaves in the lower part. Purplish-black fruit, to ½ in. across, ripening in September, has a winy, bittersweet, aromatic flavor; often made into liquor. The tree is severely attacked by tent caterpillars, the webs being conspicuously present in spring. Lustrous brown, strong, close-grained wood is prized for furniture. The aromatic bark has tonic, flavoring, and medicinal qualities.

WHITE OAK

Quercus alba **Beech Family**

DISTRIBUTED over most of the eastern U. S. in upland woods and fields, this mighty oak sometimes grows to well over 100 ft., usually lower in the open, with stout, wide-spreading limbs. Bark gray, in small, scaly plates. Leaves to 9 in., with 5 to 9 blunt lobes ; rosy-tinted when young, purplish in autumn ; long-persistent. Ovoid-oblong acorn, to 1 in. long, enclosed by shallow, thin, stalked cup. Wood highly prized for timbers, shipbuilding, interior finish, furniture, etc. Bark used in tanning. The CHESTNUT OAK *(Q. montana)* inhabits rocky streambanks, hillsides, and woods in a more limited area in the East, likewise forming a broad, loose crown. Generally short-trunked, with dark brown bark showing widely spaced, longish, irregular corky ridges. Unlobed leaves to 7 in., with coarse, roundish teeth ; shiny green above in summer, orange-russet in autumn. Acorn ovoid, to 1½ in. long, about half-enclosed in top-shaped cup ; 1 or 2 on a stalk. Wood used for railroad ties ; bark for tanning.

51

RED OAK

Quercus borealis   **Beech Family**

In RICH uplands and hillsides, to 100 ft. high, with large, round, loose crown, and tall, clear trunk. Bark dark grayish-brown, with long, vertical, flattish ridges. Twigs red. Leaves to 9 in., oblong, with 7 to 11 fine-pointed, deep lobes ; dark red in autumn. Acorn ovoid, to 1 in. long, one-third cup-enclosed ; 1 or 2 on a short stalk ; ripens the second year. Wood valuable. Bark rich in tannic acid. The POST OAK (*Q. stellata*), of sandy and rocky places, forms in the open a dense, round crown ; generally less than 60 ft. high. Bark a red-brown block-pattern of small plates. Obovate leaves, to 8 in., with 3 large squarish upper lobes and usually 2 smaller lobes farther down ; dark, leathery ; russet in autumn ; hanging on in winter. Acorn to 1 in., one-third to half enclosed. Wood used for fence posts. The OVER-CUP OAK (*Q. lyrata*) is a wet-land tree, with round, short trunk. Slender leaves have 6 to 10 roundish- to blunt-tipped lobes ; bright green above, white-downy below. Acorn almost entirely enclosed. Wood as valuable as White Oak.

PIN OAK

Quercus palustris   **Beech Family**

OCCURRING mostly in coastal plains, valleys,
and bottom lands in the eastern U.S., the Pin
Oak raises its undivided stem often to 75—
sometimes to more than 100—ft. high, with
slender, closely spaced lateral branches. Young
crowns pyramidal, with lower branches pendulous, upper horizontal. Bark dark gray, super-
ficially ridged on old trunks, smoothish on
young. Twigs reddish-brown to orange-brown.
Leaves 3 to 5 in. long, with 5 to 7 pointed lobes
having pointed teeth or sub-lobes; lustrous
green above, paler below, with only axillary
tufts of hairs; autumn color varies from year
to year—sometimes lacking, sometimes a brilliant red. Roundish acorns to ½ in. long, less
than half-enclosed by cup; 1 or more on stalk;
ripening the second year. Wood used for interior finish, shingles, etc. Very similar, but with
broader crown, is the SCARLET OAK (*Q. coc-
cinea*) inhabiting drier, lighter soils. Autumn
color always a brilliant red. Acorns to 4/5 in.
long, about half cup-enclosed. Wood used for
furniture, interior finish, etc.

53

WILLOW OAK

Quercus phellos   **Beech Family**

THIS oak inhabits swamp margins and moist sandy flats in the Southeast and along the Atlantic Coast, growing to about 80 ft. high and forming in the open a pyramidal, round-topped crown. Bark on old trees reddish-brown, with narrow ridges. Leaves not toothed or lobed, suggestive of willow leaves (hence its name) ; 2 to 4 in. long; lustrous green in summer, pale yellow in autumn. Acorn hemispherical, about 2/5 in. long, held in very shallow cup. Wood used mainly for charcoal and fuel. The SHINGLE OAK (*Q. imbricaria*), found in rich bottom lands in the central-eastern U. S., sometimes grows to 100 ft. in the woods, generally lower in the open, with short trunk and irregularly pyramidal crown. Bark pale brown, with narrow ridges. Leaves blunt or pointed, not toothed or lobed ; to 6 in. long ; lustrous green above, brownish- or whitish-downy below, brownish-red in autumn. Acorn hemispherical, to 2/5 in. long, one-third to half cup-enclosed. Wood used for interior finish, clapboards, shingles, and furniture.

BLACK LOCUST
Yellow Locust

Robinia pseudoacacia   **Pea Family**

THIS largest of our locusts (to 80 ft.) grows on gravelly slopes of the Appalachians, from Pennsylvania southward. Widely planted and naturalized, it generally remains lower, spreading from suckering roots. It rapidly forms a graceful young tree with oblong crown; ultimately generally narrower to cylindrical, less graceful, with short, gaunt, stout, brittle branches. Bark brown, deeply grooved between thick, boldly braided ridges. Leaves alternate, pinnate, flanked by spines; to 14 in. long. 7 to 19 leaflets, to 2 in. long, minutely notched at the apex; rather pale green in summer, at least partly yellow in autumn or dull gray after heavy frost. Creamy-white flowers shaped like those of the pea; in drooping clusters to 8 in. long, appearing in late May or June, their fragrance perfuming the air. Pods flattened, to 4 in. long, with 3 or more seeds; hanging on in winter. Hard, yellowish wood used in shipbuilding, for posts and ties, etc. Bark of roots has medicinal qualities.

PUSSY WILLOW

Salix discolor   **Willow Family**

USUALLY a roundish-topped shrub, occasionally a short-trunked, narrow tree to about 20 ft. high. Twigs rather robust. Reddish buds slender, pointed. Elliptic- to oblong-lance-shaped leaves to 4 in. long, pointed at both ends, irregularly or not at all toothed; thick and firm; green on upper side, whitish-silky below. Spikes precede leaves in early spring, the female to 1 in. long, when unfolding whitish- to grayish-silky (this is the Pussy Willow which children love to pick early in spring). Twigs cut in winter may easily be forced into bloom indoors in water. The SANDBAR WILLOW (*S. longifolia*) is abundant on low, sandy riverbanks, often the first woody growth to take hold on newly formed sand bars. Usually a thicket-forming shrub of variable height, occasionally a narrow little tree to about 20 ft. high. Twigs orange to purplish-red. Lance-shaped leaves to 4 in. long, pointed and sparsely toothed; bright green. Spikes appear simultaneously with leaves. Wood of no appreciable value.

BLACK WILLOW

Salix nigra   **Willow Family**

WIDELY distributed in the U. S., occurring
along margins of trees, lakes, and swamps,
this willow, sometimes shrubby, more often
forms a tree to 35 ft. high, with trunk branched
at or near base. Twigs yellowish. Old bark
brown, with coarse, rough, scaly plates. Narrowly lance-shaped leaves finely saw-toothed;
ultimately hairless, except sometimes on the
veins above; green above, paler green below.
Stipules heart-shaped and broad. Male spikes
to 2 in., female to 3, appear at same time as
leaves. Wood used mainly for fuel. The GOLD-
EN WILLOW *(S. alba,* var. *vitellina)* is an Old
World willow widely naturalized in the U. S.,
its golden-yellow twigs often lending a warm
glow to waterside landscapes in winter. Sometimes reaching a height of 75 ft., it forms a
wide, roundish crown with outer branches
somewhat pendulous, the trunk often divided
at the base. Bark brown, deeply furrowed.
Branchlets yellow. Narrow pointed leaves,
green above, pale-bluish below. Light, soft
wood used mainly for charcoal and fuel.

57

SASSAFRAS

Sassafras albidum   **Laurel Family**

OFTEN abundant in fringes of woods on rich, sandy soils, suckering from the roots. Sometimes to 100 ft. high, with stout, short, clear stem ; usually lower in open, often at first with taller, irregular, flat- or round-topped crown of varying width ; nearly always picturesque. All parts are aromatic. Bark ultimately reddish-brown, furrowed between thick, broad, often corky ridges. Twigs smooth and green. Buds greenish, pointed, ovate. Leaves alternate, to 7 in. long, entire or 3- to 5-lobed, apex blunt or pointed ; bright green above, bluish below, brilliant orange and scarlet in autumn. Small yellow flowers appear with leaves, in short terminal clusters ; male and female on separate trees. Bluish-black ovoid, stoned fruit relished by birds. Soft, coarse, brownish-yellow wood used in boatbuilding, in cooperage, for fences ; formerly for ox yokes. Bark yields an oil employed in flavoring medicines ; that of root makes a medicinal tea.

AMERICAN MOUNTAIN ASH

Sorbus americana   Rose Family

THIS bright-fruited tree grows in swamp margins and moist, rich soils in the eastern U. S.; sometimes shrubby, it is usually a tree to about 30 ft. high, with narrow crown. Trunk rarely over 1 ft. thick. Bark smooth, lustrous brownish-gray with horizontal lenticels (slits). Twigs smooth, brownish. Alternate, pinnate leaves, 6 to 12 in. long; 9 to 17 leaflets, to 4 in. long, oblong-lance-shaped, with pointed apex, sharply saw-toothed, yellow-green and hairless above, paler below, downy when young. Leafstalks generally red. Small, numerous, creamy-white flowers, in dense, flattish clusters to 6 in. across appear in late May or June. Large clusters of scarlet, roundish, berrylike fruit, to ¼ in. diam., tipped with a dry calyx, ripen in September, remaining colorful for a long time and hanging on in winter in a blackened condition, when birds gladly eat them. Soft, pale brown wood of little economic value.

Index and Key to Range of Trees in This Book

Note: The map (page 4) represents only an approximation of the distribution range of the trees indexed. Certain species may often be found outside the areas accredited to them; other species, due to various unfavorable conditions, may be missing in parts of areas accredited to them. The capital letters indicate the general area of distribution on the accompanying map.